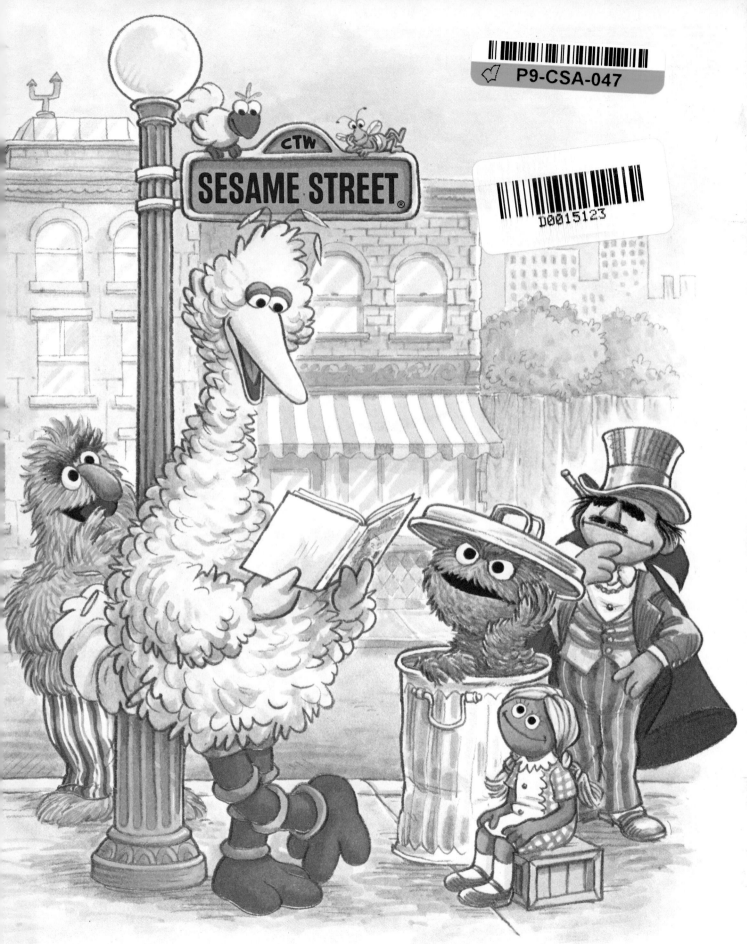

CTW

SESAME STREET®

Joe Mathieu

THE
SESAME STREET®
LIBRARY

With Jim Henson's Muppets

VOLUME 10

FEATURING
THE LETTER T
AND THE NUMBER
10

Children's Television Workshop/Funk & Wagnalls, Inc.

WRITTEN BY:

Michael Frith
Jerry Juhl
Emily Perl Kingsley
David Korr
Sharon Lerner
Nina B. Link
Albert G. Miller
Jeffrey Moss
Norman Stiles
Jon Stone
Daniel Wilcox

ILLUSTRATED BY:

Mel Crawford
A. Delaney
Mary Lou Dettmer
Michael Frith
Joseph Mathieu
Michael J. Smollin
Bob Taylor

PHOTOGRAPHS BY:

Charles P. Rowan

0-8343-0018-4   3 4 5 6 7 8 9 0

T t

The Terrible Tickler

*The whole town of Tombstone remembers the day
That the Terrible Tickler came riding their way.
He came down the street with a look keen and steady
And said, "Folks, my tickling finger is ready.
Now tickling's terrific and tickling is fun,
And you'll all be tickled before I am done.
For tickling's my pleasure, my greatest of joys.
I think I'll start off with the young girls and boys!"*

He first tickled Teddy,
Then Mike, Fran and Sue,
Then Manuel and Mary
And Algernon, too.
Not one could escape,
Though they'd run and they'd wriggle—
Each one would get tickled
And fall down and giggle.
And soon not a boy
Or a girl could be found
Except those who lay
Laughing down on the ground.

"I've got all the kids. Now it's time for the others,"
The Tickler announced. "Next come fathers and mothers."

So the Terrible Tickler
Went on with his work.
He got Nina the plumber
And Charlie the clerk.
He got Sam the barber
And even the mayor
Who fell laughing and giggling
Right out of his chair.

And as sure as five pennies add up to one nickel,
There wasn't one grownup that he didn't tickle.
"I've tickled the people but still I'm not through."
Said the Terrible Tickler, "Now guess what I'll do."

Well, he tickled the horses
And tickled the cows,
He tickled the cats
Till they giggled meows.
He tickled the pigs
And the mules and the dogs.
And he tickled the chickens
And even the frogs.

Then he looked all around and said, "I'm in a pickle.
I'm done and there's nobody left here to tickle.
I've tickled them all now," he said with a frown.
"I guess I'll just have to go find a new town!"
So he tickled a doll sitting high on a shelf.
Then he rode out of town as he tickled—himself.

And everyone said with a giggle and sigh,
"That Terrible Tickler's a mean rotten guy."
And they heard him call back as he giggled with glee,
"Remember that tickle begins with a T."

Little Red Riding Hood

Little Red Riding Hood was taking a basket of food to her grandmother when a wolf walked up to her. "Where are you going, pretty little girl?" asked the wolf sweetly.

Red Riding Hood knew she was not supposed to speak to strangers. But she did anyway.

"I'm going to see my grandma," she said. "She lives over there, in the woods."

"How nice," said the wolf and he ran straight to the grandmother's house and locked the old lady in the closet.

When Red Riding Hood arrived, the wolf was in the grandmother's bed, dressed up in her nightgown and cap. Little Red Riding Hood said:

"Why, Grandma, what big ears you have!"

"The better to hear you with, my dear," said the wolf.

"Grandma, what big teeth you have!"

"The better to eat you with!" cried the wolf, leaping out of bed. When Red Riding Hood saw who it was, she screamed.

Luckily a woodsman was passing, and heard her. He leaned through the window and killed the wolf.

Little Red Riding Hood thanked him and together they let the grandmother out of the closet. After that, Red Riding Hood never spoke to strangers again.

Bert's 10 Collections

Ernie! Ernie!
Come quickly. I've finally
finished my ten collections.
Now I have a separate
collection for each of the
numbers from one to ten.
Oh! It's so exciting!

That's
great, Bert! Let
me see!

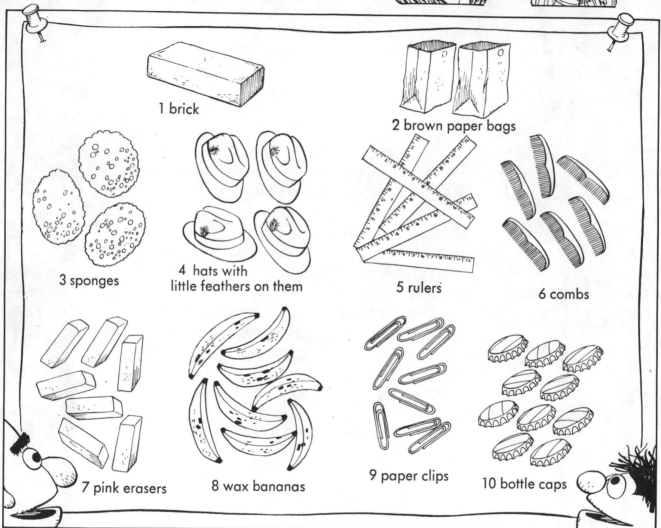

1 brick

2 brown paper bags

3 sponges

4 hats with
little feathers on them

5 rulers

6 combs

7 pink erasers

8 wax bananas

9 paper clips

10 bottle caps

You see,
I finally finished it
when I found the Figgy-Fizz
top for my bottle cap
collection. That makes
TEN, and . . .
Ernie?

Ernie? Oh,
wake up,
Ernie.

The Count's Birthday Party

Greetings! It is I, the Count. Bert and Ernie have brought me a birthday present. It is a lovely 1 and a beautiful 2.

Here are my presents from Sherlock, Grover and Betty Lou. Just what I always wanted! A 3, a 4, and a 5.

Look! Look! Presents from Roosevelt and his mother, and from Herbert! 6, 7 and 8!

And from Cookie Monster! And from Granny Fanny! 9 and 10! It's wonderful! WONDERFUL!

Now it is time for the party. But first, let us count the guests . . . 1,2,3, 4,5,6,7,8,9,10. Now let us count the presents . . . 1,2,3, 4,5,6,7,8,9,10. Now let us count the candles . . . Isn't this fun? 1,2,3,4,5,6,7,8,9,10 . . .

The King of Cauliflower's Castle

Once upon a time, in the Kingdom of Cauliflower, there was a King. The King lived in a very nice castle. But the King was not satisfied.

Soon, the royal workpeople were hard at work, building the King a bigger castle.

And the castle grew and grew ...

... and grew, until it went right up to the edge of the
Kingdom of Cauliflower in every direction. In the
North, it touched the fence between Cauliflower and
the land of Rutabaga. In the South, it bumped right
into the United States of Spinach. In the West, it cast
its shadow on the good people of Broccoli. And in the
East, it looked right down on the hills and valleys
of Canteloupe.

But the castle was *so* big, there was no room *outside* in the land of Cauliflower. The whole land of Cauliflower was *inside* the castle. And that caused problems. The King's cows couldn't find any grass to eat. . . .

And His Highness's hens and the royal rooster couldn't find any bugs or seeds to eat.

And His Highness's horse had no place to run around.

So what do you think happened next?

But, oh dear, His Majesty's mackerels and the Queen's quackers were in the bathtub, because there weren't any more lakes and rivers in Cauliflower. And even worse...

...all the Royal Staircases were covered with flower pots.

So the King ordered the Carpenter to make the castle smaller. Then there would be room outside for Princess Peony's flowers, and the cows and the hens and the horse would come back. "And then," yelled the King, "you can get the fish out of my bathtub!"

And so, the royal workpeople took the big new castle apart and put back the old small one. And sure enough, the cows came back, and the chickens came back, and the horse came back . . .

But the King of Cauliflower had learned a very important lesson—BIGGER is not always BETTER.

Bert Brings You...

Build a Better Bird Feeder

Hello! Welcome! Welcome to the weekly meeting of the Sesame Street Pigeon Lovers Club. This week we are going to talk about making a bird feeder for ALL our feathered friends.

Making a bird feeder is easy. All you need is an empty milk carton. First, have someone cut a hole in it, like this.

Punch a hole in the top and tie a piece of string to it.

Put some birdseed or bread crumbs in it and hang it up on a tree, or a fire escape, or out your window. Then you can watch the little birdies in your neighborhood as they hop in and out of your milk carton bird feeder looking for their supper.

Of course, in OUR neighborhood we have to do things a little differently . . .

J. Mathieu

Jack be nimble, Jack be quick,
Jack jump over the candlestick.

THE BOY, THE GIRL AND THE JELLYBEANS

CHAPTER THREE

Early one evening, a boy who was crazy about jellybeans was walking down the street feeling very angry. That morning he had given his jellybeans to a girl he'd met. And that afternoon he had just gotten the jellybeans back when a monster came along and ate them all up. So the boy had lost his jellybeans twice in one day, and just thinking about it made him very, very mad.

"Boy, am I mad," he said to himself as he walked along. "If you lose your jellybeans once it makes you sad. But if you lose them twice it makes you *mad*. Now all I have left is my empty jellybean bag. No *wonder* I'm mad."

Just then he turned the corner, and there he saw the girl he had given his jellybeans to that morning. In front of her was a table with a pile of jellybeans on it and she was talking angrily to herself.

"Boy, am I mad," the girl said. "I'm so angry I could *scream*. I think I *will* scream." And she did and the boy heard her, because it was so loud.

"Hey," said the boy. "Why are you screaming like that?"

"Because I'm *mad,*" she grumped. "I'm in a rotten mood."

"Me, too," scowled the boy. "And I bet I'm madder than you are."

"Ha!" she snorted. "That's what you think. You don't know what mad *is* until you're as mad as I am."

"Yeah? What're you so mad about?"

"I found these jellybeans. I thought I'd lost them, but I found them right here on the table."

The boy frowned. "That's why you're mad? That's nothing to be *mad* about."

"I'm not mad about *finding* these jellybeans," she shouted. "I'm mad because *I don't have anything to put them in!* So I can't take them home."

"Why not eat them here?" the boy suggested.

"How can I? It's almost dinnertime. If I eat these jellybeans now, they'll spoil my dinner. So I'll just have to stay here forever and ever looking at them, because I don't have anything to put them in and *that's* why I'm mad."

"Phooey," said the boy, "that's nothing. Let me tell you what *I'm* mad about. I lost my jellybeans twice today—once to you and once to a monster. And I'll never get them back because the monster ate them, and so all I have is an empty jellybean bag and that's why I'm mad."

"Well," said the girl, "that's nothing to be mad ab–" She stopped and looked at the boy. "You have an *empty* jellybean bag?"

"Sure, but what difference does–?" The boy pointed at the table. "*You* have jellybeans?"

"Yes, I have," she said sweetly.

He smiled. "What do you know? I have a bag to put them in."

"Hey," she said, "I'm not mad anymore."

"Neither am I."

The girl laughed. "Hey, want to come to my house for dinner?"

"Sure," said the boy, "but–uh– what're we going to have?"

"Jellybeans, of course. Okay?"

"O-*kay!* Here . . . pour your jellybeans into my bag," said the boy. And she did.

And so there were jellybeans for everybody! Isn't that a good way to end the story?

THE END !

This is your old friend Grover here explaining two words FAR . . . . . . and NEAR.

So here I go like a racing car . . .

I stand way off— we call this FAR!

I run right back like a speeding deer . . .

Now I am close. We call this NEAR!

I zoom once more like a shooting star . . .

. . . and from where you sit I am quite FAR!

When I run back from there to here . . .

. . . and stand beside you I am NEAR!

Again I leave you where you are and run like mad till I am . . .

FAR!

I gallop back till I am . . .

NEAR!

What has four feet, stripes and
eats popcorn in the zoo?

Bert and Ernie!

Grover Buys Ten Balloons

10
Ten
tiny toy tops.

1
One
wobbly wombat.

Two
tweeting
Twiddlebugs. **2**

9
Nine
nice nose nests.

Big Bird's Beak Breakers

I have a beak-breaker for every number from one to ten. See if you can say each one three times quickly.

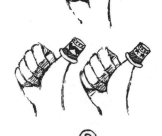

3
Three
thick thumb
thimbles.

8
Eight
great grape
graters.

Oh, dear!
I don't think my beak will ever be the same!

4
Four
fake fairies
fall flat.

7
Seven
snickering snails.

5
Five
funny feathered
fire fighters.

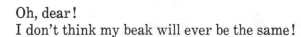

6
Six
she-seals sell seashells.